The Brook

by Carol and Donald Carrick

The Brook

THE MACMILLAN COMPANY, NEW YORK • COLLIER-MACMILLAN LIMITED, LONDON

For Christopher,
    who came on the first warm day

Spring rain floods the land,
running down the mountain roof.

Ice fingers poke deep into rock and drip meltwater.

Springs rise in the swampy grass,
and collect in wandering rivulets
that trickle down dark hollows.

The deer drink,
raise their heads to listen,
and leave tiptoe marks
in the late drifts.

The young brook bores
through the high pasture,
sweeping over stones.

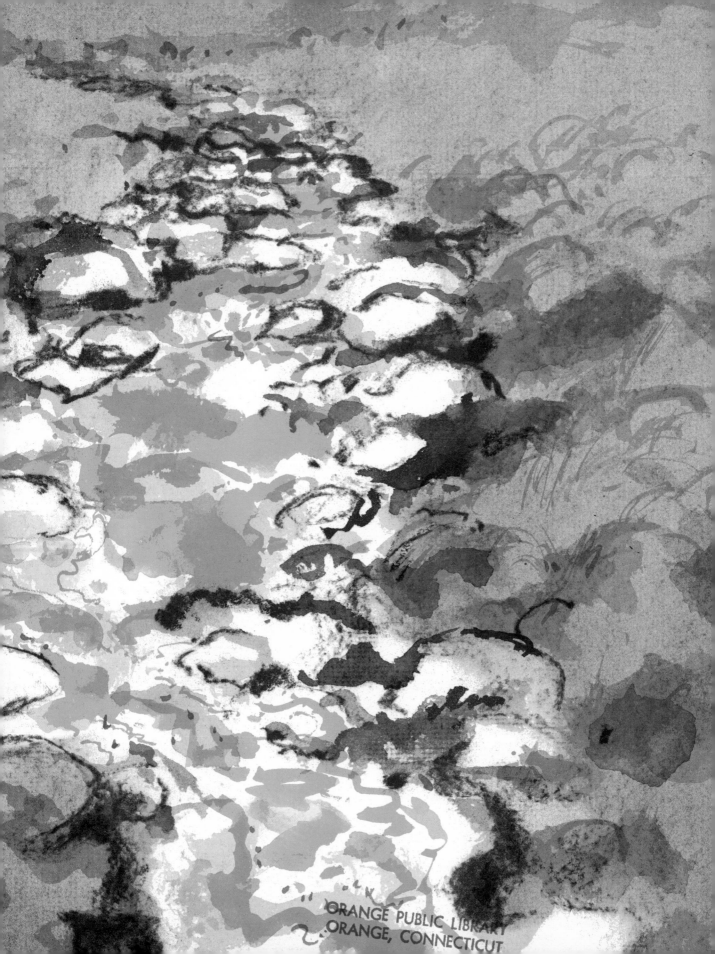

It spills in narrow falls,
spitting
and splashing
and splattering.

With a roar the brook plunges
in whitening rapids,

down broad steps,
through a tunnel of trees.

The brook bubbles down
through a forest,
which muffles its water song.

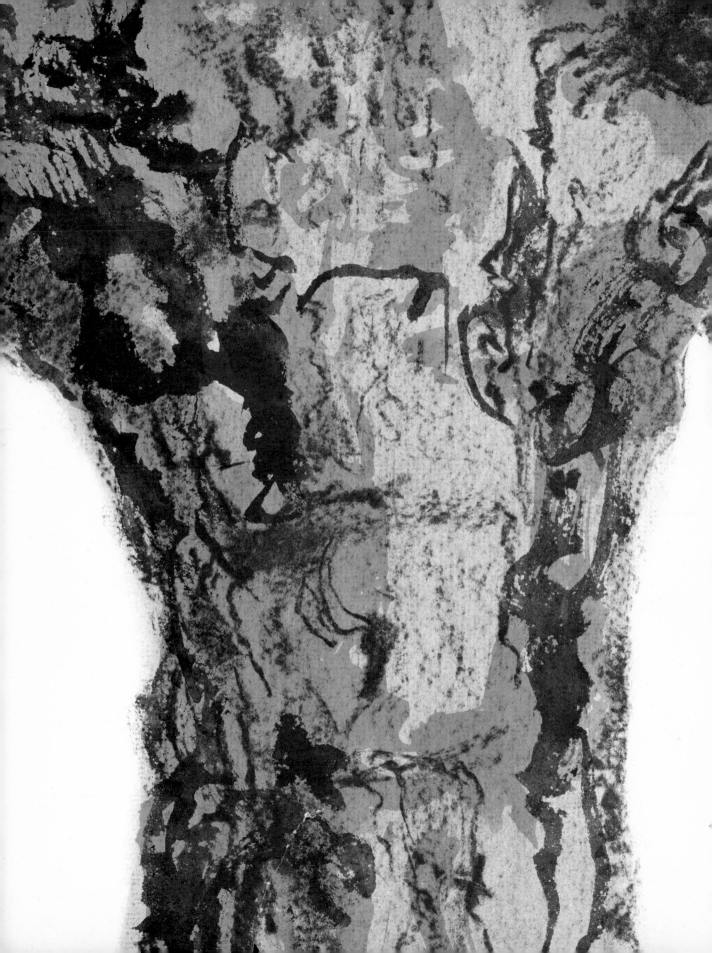

Overhead
the woodpecker
hammers,
and showers
bright chips
that bob
on the ripples.

Sunlight warms the backs of rocks
and freckles ferns and crusted bark.

Shadows of trout dart
from dark caverns
and drift over silvery gravel.

A water bird wades
through reflections of reeds,
searching, alone,
for its evening meal.

Silently,
shallow and slow,
the brook
slides into the pond.
Together
they flow to the sea.